# SP🔦T
## the DIFFERENCE

Art Director: Tammy Desnoyers
Design: Rafaela Petel Ruiz
Images: © Freepik, © Shutterstock

**PAPP International Inc.**
**3700 Griffith Street, Suite 395,**
**Montreal (Quebec), Canada  H4T 2B3**

**PáPP**™
publishing

www.pappinternational.com

# FIND THE 8 CHANGES & KEEP SCORE.

☐☐☐☐☐☐☐☐

# FIND THE 9 CHANGES & KEEP SCORE.

# PUZZLE 3

## FIND THE *6* CHANGES & KEEP SCORE.

□ □ □ □ □ □

ANSWERS ON PAGE 30

# PUZZLE 4

## ONE OF THESE IS NOT LIKE THE OTHERS.
## CAN YOU SPOT THE DIFFERENCE ?

ANSWER ON PAGE 30

# FIND THE 6 CHANGES & KEEP SCORE.

☐ ☐ ☐ ☐ ☐ ☐

# FIND THE 7 CHANGES & KEEP SCORE.

☐ ☐ ☐ ☐ ☐ ☐ ☐

ANSWERS ON PAGE 31

# FIND THE 8 CHANGES & KEEP SCORE.

# PUZZLE 8

## FIND THE 10 CHANGES & KEEP SCORE.

ANSWERS ON PAGE 31

# PUZZLE 9

## ONE OF THESE IS NOT LIKE THE OTHERS.
## CAN YOU SPOT THE DIFFERENCE?

ANSWER ON PAGE 31

# FIND THE 7 CHANGES & KEEP SCORE.

☐ ☐ ☐ ☐ ☐ ☐ ☐

# PUZZLE 11

## ONE OF THESE IS NOT LIKE THE OTHERS.
## CAN YOU SPOT THE DIFFERENCE?

ANSWER ON PAGE 31

# PUZZLE 12

## ONE OF THESE IS NOT LIKE THE OTHERS.
## CAN YOU SPOT THE DIFFERENCE?

ANSWER ON PAGE 31

# PUZZLE 14

## FIND THE 7 CHANGES & KEEP SCORE.

☐ ☐ ☐ ☐ ☐ ☐ ☐

ANSWERS ON PAGE 32

# PUZZLE 15

## ONE OF THESE IS NOT LIKE THE OTHERS.
## CAN YOU SPOT THE DIFFERENCE?

ANSWER ON PAGE 32

# FIND THE 7 CHANGES & KEEP SCORE.

# FIND THE 9 CHANGES & KEEP SCORE.

☐ ☐ ☐ ☐ ☐ ☐ ☐ ☐ ☐

# ANSWERS

### PUZZLE 1 | Page 3

### PUZZLE 2 | Page 5

### PUZZLE 3 | Page 6

### PUZZLE 4 | Page 7

### PUZZLE 5 | Page 9

### PUZZLE 6 | Page 11

## PUZZLE 7 | Page 13

## PUZZLE 8 | Page 14

## PUZZLE 9 | Page 15

## PUZZLE 10 | Page 17

## PUZZLE 11 | Page 18

## PUZZLE 12 | Page 19

PUZZLE 13 | **Page 21**

PUZZLE 14 | **Page 22**

PUZZLE 16 | **Page 25**

PUZZLE 15 | **Page 23**

PUZZLE 17 | **Page 27**

PUZZLE 18 | **Page 29**